Sarah's Collection

A Collection of Original
Poems, Quotes, and A Short Story

Sarah's Collection

A Collection of Original
Poems, Quotes, and A Short Story

Sarah Lauren English

SLE Publishing
Dallas, Texas

Unless otherwise indicated, all scriptural quotations are from the *King James Version* of the Bible.

Sarah's Collections — A Collection of Original Poems, Quotes, and A Short Story
Published by:
SLE Publishing
P.O. Box 570795
Dallas, TX 75357
ISBN 0-971491-2-7

Cover design by and book production by:
Double Blessing Productions
P.O. Box 52756, Tulsa, OK 74152

Printed in the United States of America.

Contents

Dedication

The purpose of love, life, and loss...
My Cry...1
Cold Wata 4

In the midst of a conquest to superiority...
Is It Funny? 7
I Am But A Woman 8
Dream, Dreaming, Dreamed 9
Big Imagination 10
My Imagination...15

Now I can fly, I have wings...
Mixed-Up Colors 18

Regardless of the inhumanity of the world...
Essence 20
God's Fingertips..22
Love Yourself..23
Sun-Kissed Angels 25

Family bonds are the strongest...
The Love of a Daughter 28
Afro 30
Silly Girl..32

To guide you emotions, know your heart...

Stealer of My Heart 35

5:20 36

Smiles and grins that come from within...

The Fee of Love Deferred.....................................40

Love Me..42

You can't experience true pleasure...

The Tears of Summer..44

Can You Hear Them? 45

Our stars are dying to meet...

To Love Once..47

Wish I May, Wish I Might......................................49

Mind travels beyond humanity...

Soft Rain...52

As I lay in the darkness...

Dancing Light 55

Reaching for the Stars 56

Heavy eyelids bring serenity

Sarah 59

Good night to all my stars...

Dedication

I dedicate this book to my darling, little cousins whom I love because your smiles lift my soul. You are my sun-kissed angels...

The purpose of love, life, and loss is a mystery,
But through experience, revelations unfold
And secrets can be told
Because the sunshine brings butterflies
And there can be no more cries.

My Cry

(For: Ava Wilson, whose knowledge, beauty, and strength is pure and outstanding.)

Holding on to thoughts
Clinging to dreams
Wishing they wouldn't seem
All for naught

How I wish I could fly
And travel beyond the skies
Forever singing
Until your ear is ringing
With my song:

My styles always changing
Makes you confused
My rhythm always moving
Leaves you two steps behind
And I'm three ahead of you
At reading that, you confined
Your imagination into reality
But once you understand spirituality
And free the frames of your mentality
You'll take a step closer to me
Hopefully
you'll comprehend my cries
"I WANT TO BE FREE!"
Not from shackles and chains
But mentally and economically
Will you ever understand my slavery?
Yet you pass "proclamations" saying I

Could go free
But you didn't tell me
Now I have to ask for land
That my forefathers tilled by hand

Still you don't understand
That I shouldn't have to demand
To see my African sand
Forced me away from my motherland
You wonder why they don't trust you
You wanted the cake to eat it, too
Always mixing with other colors
Burned and hung my brothers
True, true
Upset when you heard we knew
What you were up to
Planning to destroy us
Yet, "In God we trust"?
Would God promote this negativity
That you claim is humanity?
But I believe to be insanity
Allowed hatred to replace your heart
Never wanted "integration" from the start
Now my people are puppets for you
You got Mumia and Assata, too
Only physically
'Cause mentally
They are free
Still, I have distant cries
For my people who are hypnotized
And whose soul can no longer fly
Attached to your money
Like bees on honey
Nikki Giovanni said,
"Black love is black wealth"

So let's birth unity
  And balance it with purity
  Our history section in your books
  Is sugar-coated
  So we won't know the truth
  You didn't want our knowledge to grow
  Our ancient African names – we'll never know
  But I'll remain to uphold the truth
  People of all colors, know your roots
  And I will....

Hold on to thoughts
  Cling to dreams
  Wishing they wouldn't seem
  All for naught

How I wish I could fly
  And travel beyond the skies
  Forever going to sing
  Until my people are happy beings
  So in your ears, my voice will ring
  Always ring...
  My voice will always ring

Cold Wata

Eyes watering
'Cuz of onion peels
Ouch!
It burns
My eyes is burnin'
Mama said,
"Get some cold wata
It'll be alright"

Tears kissing cheeks
'cuz Daddy got hung
He outside my door
Mama just a-cryin'
And screamin',
"Kill them crackaz
Kill them crackaz!"
Rest your mind
Get some cold wata
It'll be alright

Screams comin' from my belly
Don't wanna go
Mama says I got to, though
So I'z can see what they did to my
...Daddy
Please don't leave me all alone
Daddy died
Mama cried

Get some cold wata
It'll be alright

Eyes watering
  Mouth opened
  Mama get up from there
  Stop jivin', Mama
  It ain't funny no mo'
  Why your eyes white?
  Mama?
  No...
  No...
  Sista said,
  "Get some cold wata
  It'll be alright"

Two funerals in a week
  Mouth stuck shut
  Can't even speak
  White man came said we got to go
  Don't separate us
  Keep us together
  Looking down from heaven,
  Daddy cried
  Because
  Mama died
  Cracka said,
  "Get some cold wata
  It'll be alright"

*I*n the midst of a conquest to superiority, one can become the victims of an easily-attained venom. They care not of other people's feelings, and start indulging in the existence of their own beings; they forget their own internal blemishes and point out everyone else's.

Why beholdest thou the mote that is in thy brother's eye, but considerest not the beam that is in thine own eye.

Matthew 7:3 (KJV)

Is It Funny?

My life seems to have gone
It is not in my control
Doesn't this picture seem wrong?
A fragment is untold
Where is my pride?
And how I used to stride
Everything seems to mock
My very being
And in my ears the words are ringing
Is it true what everyone is saying?
I feel my pride and esteem decaying
I am now the topic to discuss
And I don't know whom to trust
You see I slipped and sinned
Now I will never hear the end
Inside I grieve painfully
And you look at me
Disapprovingly
When you make a mistake
Put yourself in my place
And see if you'll erase
The little smirk on your face
Am I laughing at your imperfections?
When's the last time you've been to confession?
Remember this phrase that will surely help you:
"What would Jesus do?"

I Am But A Woman

I am but a woman
Full of hopes and dreams
Some will be shattered
Yet, some will be seen
But I will keep the faith
Yes I will believe
Because I am but a woman
Full of hopes and dreams

Dream, Dreaming, Dreamed

*D*reaming to be more
This is our goal
What we're dreaming for
Will never be known
If we watch our lives pass us by
Wondering what happened and why

Open doors make themselves known
And all the meanwhile, we sit and groan
Never doing anything with what God gave
Not using our gifts, that will go down in our graves

How we all dream to be more
But when shall we start?
When there's nothing to dream for?
When our "dreaming" goes to *dreamed*?
And all of our talents never seen?

Start dreaming, it's past time to begin
Because it might be too late to ever dream again

Big Imagination

(Dedicated to: Phylicia McFaddin, whose friendship and spirit can't be measured)

Hello! My name is Ruth Mae Brown, and I live in Alabama. I dream about a lot of things. Things that probably will never come true, but I still dream anyway. There's a writing contest at school, and the writer of the most interesting story about their life wins three full dollars! Well, my life is kind of interesting. So, I decided I'm going to write a story about my life and enter it in the contest.

Before I tell you the story I'm going to enter, here's a little about me, Ruth Mae. I am in the sixth grade, and I go to a public school called Rolling Plains. I live in Birmingham, Alabama and have lived here all my life, unfortunately. Sometimes I dreamed I was born in New York, but my accent gives it away. I am kind of tall and have brownie-colored skin. My hair is always in braids because momma make it that way every week. I have two other brothers and sisters. One older brother named Johnny, who's 15, and a younger sister named Shilly. Johnny is in the tenth grade and very smart. All the girls like him and giggle when he walks by. He don't look all that good to me, but he look out for me and Shilly, who is only four. Shilly's real name is Sherice Lily, but we call her Shilly for short. She look like I did when I was her age and everybody say so.

We live with our mom, Ruth Lily, and our dad, Johnny. Our house is stuffy, small, and crowded. I'm kind of sick of it because it's so boring, but I am grateful because there are some who don't have places to stay, like Milly. Milly and her ma are homeless, and they live in the shelter across the road from our house. Milly is my age and doesn't go to school because she has to look for work. She had a crush on my

10

brother because she say he "sooo sweet like a caramel apple" and "ain't never made fun of her." Milly ain't never had no caramel apple before. Anyway, I was born in July, and Milly was born in August. Once, a couple years back, we had a birthday party together because Milly ain't never had no party. Ma and me, we bake foods and cakes for Milly and her ma. Sometimes we give them money because they nice people and didn't do nothing to nobody. I like Milly a lot and she like me, too.

Our house is kind of shabby. We have lived in this old house for as long as I can remember, but I am grateful because there's folks, like Milly Walter, who ain't got nothing at all. As I've previously said.

So, I figure I have enough stuff to enter in to the contest. I might *stretch* the truth a little, just to make it even more interesting, but I think the judges will love it. Because there's nothing the matter with a big imagination, right? Well, here it goes. This is my entry:

My Story

Hello, judges. My name is Rhonda Elizabeth Mae Brown. People call me "Liz". I used to live in a big house in Beverly Hills, and I used to drink champagne and Coca-Cola with the stars. I am very famous and everybody loves me. They love me so much because I can sing the blues better than Billy Holiday. I can write better than Maya Angelou. I can preach better than the Dr. Martin Luther King, Jr. I can dance better than Sammy Davis. I can act better than Dorothy Dandridge in "Carmen Jones" or Bette Davis in "All About Eve". Yep, I can. I can because I will. You just wait and see. I am almost 12 years old. I'll be 12 on July 16. I was born July 16, 1930 in Italy, but we moved to Beverly Hills when I was still a baby.

I have an older brother named Johnny Jay. He is a lady's man. He ain't no lady's man to me because he ain't all that fine. Everybody in town thought he was the best thing since sliced bread. I remember once when me and Johnny went to the market one summer. Well, this is what happened:

"Johnny," I said as I tested the apples for ripeness. It was a warm summer day in Beverly Hills and people were bustling around us. Every three minutes someone new recognized me and asked me for my autograph, but I was worn out from all the media and press that had swamped me the day before. "Johnny, come look," I shrieked. I had just seen a worm crawling around an apple. I was very disgusted at the sight. Johnny was looking for some sugar cubes for our black stallion. You see, I would've sent my butler, Jeffrey, out to get my necessary items, but I was sick of the monstrous mansion so I decided to go myself. I said for the third time, "Johnny, come and look!"

"What is it now, Liz?" he asked, still looking for cubes.

"There's worms on the apples! Ew!" I said with distaste.

"Now, come on, Liz, just go to another apple basket. A little worm won't kill you."

12

"Okay, if you insist, Johnny, but this is very gruesome," I replied. I had very good grammar because I had my own private tutor ever since I was five years old.

Just then a young, blonde woman, who looked around 21 or so, approached Johnny, who was only 14 at the time. She started asking him questions like – if he was a model or if he was married. He acted as if he were 25 years old, but he did it with class. She asked him to marry her right on the spot! He said yes, and they smooched in front of everyone! The next day they got married in Hollywood. Come to find out my sister-in-law, a very pretty woman, was Marilyn Monroe! Don't be jealous.

Yes, I have done many things in my life where I just got to meet everybody. I had a slumber party at The White House. I won me an Emmy for the best female actress of the year. I have won a Pulitzer Prize for my album, but I don't want to brag. All this fashion and fame done got me all big and famous, I just don't know what to do with myself. It is an honor and a privilege for people to be *my* friend. As I said before I was born in Rome, Italy. We moved down here when I was still little, but I feel like I am a true Italian. My great-grandfather Vincenzo always made me spaghetti the true Italian way. Hollywood life done got me a lot of attention and fame. I just can't handle it. The truth is all this award-winning I done did has gotten me tired. That's why I live here. We, my family and I, needed to take a break, but you probably still will see me in the headlines because I still do a little movie here and there for publicity's sake. Clark Gable says he misses me in Hollywood so much that he will pay me $10,000 dollars just to go back, but I say, "It's not in my contract, Clark." I helped direct *Gone with the Wind*. Clark begged me to, so I had to say yes. One day, once my school-life has ended, I'll go back to Hollywood because Alfred Hitchcock says, "Hollywood isn't the same without you, Liz." I've also recently written a book. It's called "My Entry To The Judges". I've actually won an Oscar for it. I'm always in the Headlines...you just keep a look out. You'll see. Well, I must go because Jeffrey is calling. Thank you so very much!

So that's my story that I had entered into the contest. The word's out. I didn't win. Louisa May Alcott won with her book, "Little Women". The judges said my story was very good, but not realistic enough. They said I got the awards mixed up, and there is no way that I know all them stars and am still down here. That's okay though because I think my story was very nice. I have many things that I still got to do anyway. For one, I have to look after my friend, Milly, because nobody does. A lot of people just walk by her and her ma and don't say nothing at all. They either just ignore them and act like they don't see them or they just look at them funny, but not me. No, not Ruth or **Rhonda**.

But I don't think my job imagining is over. I'll still believe I was born in Italy because there's nothing wrong with a big imagination, right? And one day I will be drinking champagne and Coca-Cola with the stars!

My Imagination

(Dedicated to: Erica Rhodes, whose talent, beauty, and mind are always blossoming.)

My imagination is perfect for me
It travels beyond what humans can see
Originality
Emerges from my spirituality

Knowledge is a factor in my attraction
You must gain some before interaction
I'm flying
And you're tarrying
I'm smiling
And you're staring
So I leave you behind
While I imagine people in my mind
And with my thoughts they appear
Whispering sweet-nothings in my ear

My imagination is too much for you
And as my silhouette fades into the blue
You try to understand me
You may even call it insanity
Yet my mind elevates beyond humanity
You're intimidated by my creativity
Angered because my color doesn't limit me
See, I unbalance your equation
Because of the revelations
I attain

Through aware friends and books – I gain
  A knowledge that will always remain

America tries to brainwash my youth
  Still, I will remember to uphold my roots
  And be known as living proof
  The true, compelling essence of me
  Travels beyond what your limited eyes
Can see

Now I can fly
I have wings
God has given me wings
I touch heaven with my fingertips

Mixed-Up Colors

(Dedicated to: Valerie Oviedo, who brings color to my day)

Blue tears
Kiss a red face
And brown eyes
Close tightly
Because the
Purple Sun
Is too bright
Yellow grass
And green skies
Say "good-bye"
To the orange clouds
As they float up
To heaven
To see me

Regardless of the inhumanity of the world,
God still reigns.

Essence

God's mind is the world
His eyes are the oceans
And His ears are the sand
Feeling Mother Earth in His hand
Power is in His lips
Miracles on His fingertips
He controls all beings
All knowing 'cause He's all seeing
Everywhere at the same time
So don't try to hide
From Him
Just swallow your pride
Because He'll love you just the same
So bury the shame
While He erases the pain

Intimidated and doubting this truth?
Don't worry because the Book holds proof
About the God that I serve
And our love He deserves
Don't limit Him
Because you can't comprehend
How He can be a Savior and a friend
Let Him be God
And you be you
Because He'll make your life anew
Don't believe me?
I know it's true
Because when He speaks, it is so

His power can't be controlled
Confused because your science book
Didn't let you know
Stop cloning and honing
What God made
His creativity will never fade
We take our lives for granted
Thinkin' we're livin' in some kind of fairy tale
Honey, this ain't enchanted
God's love is never-ending
So stop pretending
And humble yourself
Because with His help
All is possible
He's not on a throne so high
And intangible
Have a relationship and reach
The unimaginable
Because His mind is the world
His eyes are the oceans
And his ears are the sand
Feeling Mother Earth in His hand
Power is in His lips
And miracles dance on His fingertips

God's Fingertips

In the depths of creation
There lies immense revelation
No hints of hesitation
Because God is a realization
That must come to one spiritually
Although naturally
My mind seeks
The various peaks
Of mountain tops
The river feeds off of raindrops
I am intrigued by the wonders
God's creativity asunder
Throughout the Earth
And like mothers give birth
A new being is known
God's originality is shown
These blessings
He's confessing
Are because of Him
And in a whim
Earth was made
Its beauty never fades
It will always remain
Untouched and unattained
Sweet taste of air on my lips
All of this because of God's fingertips

Love Yourself

(Dedicated to Lil' Buster)

It is often that we see
Ourselves negatively
Pointing out all the imperfections
But, we are the reflections
Of the Master's creative hand
But, what we fail to understand
Is that we are beautiful in His eye
And to Him our star always shines
"Mess-ups" is what we see
But, He looks at us mercifully
Because God's opinion
Has more dominion
Over what others have to say
We seem to think another way
We give their words power
And our esteem they devour
They are the ones that reign
But, we lack to attain
The knowledge and truth
That holds utmost proof:
If we were created by Him
He who cannot sin
What flaws did He make?
Where is His mistake?
We must learn to love what we see
And view ourselves beautifully

For our Creator thinks we matter
So, all other thoughts shatter
And, I'm happy to confess
That all negative thoughts shall be
Repressed
Because I was made by the best!

Sun-Kissed Angels

(To Sahada Weldon, who is one of my many angels,
for her true friendship, wit and words of encouragement
because they gave me peace and confidence. Shine!)

    Some are extremely lightly colored
        Others are kissed longer than the other
        We can be caramel or tan
        Depending on the Master's hand
        The sun is in love with me
        But others only temporarily
        Because tans last for a season
        I'm this color for a reason
        And I don't want to seem mean
        When I stride like a queen
        But my color doesn't limit me
        From enjoying my life freely
        But I can still hear you hiss
        All because my skin is sun-kissed

    Some say it's the color of the skin
        I say it depends on what's within
        But we do have bigger hips
        And there's magic in our lips
        Our backsides are protruding
        Our rhythm keeps you moving
        I love the kinks in our hair
        Because originality is rare
        Some use machines to get them darker
        I know they have to try a little harder
        But why must we all be classified as malicious
        And our motives seem to always be suspicious
        The objective is often missed
        All because our skin is sun-kissed

If God made the Earth, and the sun's in this
   Aren't we angels because we've been kissed?
   You thought our kiss meant ignorance
   But our ignorance had no permanence
   Because now we have education
   We're not bonded by humiliation
   Of the not-so-long ago past
   But our color will always last
   And I'm thankful for the pigment
   That you think is a predicament
   And I smile 'cause I just can't resist
   Do you wish that you were sun-kissed?

Family bonds are the strongest forms of unity
My family is the blood in my veins
And the air in my lungs
They complete me, to say the least.

The Love of a Daughter

(To: My wonderful father, whom I love dearly)

Some aren't as blessed as I have been
    Some have felt hurt over and over again
    From a man who is capable of erasing pain
    And should give sunshine during the rain
    My father is the source of my happiness
    And the reasons why I will now express:

I am the twinkle in his eye
    And because he is a Gemini
    During the storm he brings peace
    And all my confusion will cease
    Because of the wisdom he obtains
    My admiration of him will always remain

I've always gone to him with my problems
    And he always seems to solve them
    He has never judged me
    So, in my heart he will always be
    He keeps my world spinning
    And his understanding is never-ending

During the years I've cried many tears
    But he embraces me and removes my fears
    He brings warmth when I'm cold
    And the secret must be told
    He's my favorite person all the time
    And I'm so glad I can call him mine

When I lay on his big arms
  And he sings
  It does the charm
  My lips curve into a smile
  Because time with him is worthwhile

His voice soothes my ears
  And I thank God for the years
  That together we have spent
  I wonder where all the time went
  I pray Jesus grants me with more
  So my daddy and I can explore
  The depths of love forever more
  And when it's time to meet the angels
  I will rejoice because of his serene voice

I live to see your cheekbones rise
  And the twinkle in your eyes
  I love you daddy,
  My Gemini

Afro

(For Sami)

Little cousin trying to find his identity
  Picking nappy hairs
  That grow naturally
  People trying to process his originality
  "Is it long enough yet?"
  My mahogany-colored cousin asks
  Wanting to braid his curly 'fro
  And what my little cousins now know
  Is that without perms
  They're still beautiful
  Because beauty comes from within

"I ain't perming my hair!
  I ain't never gonna perm my hair!"
  Little Zack proclaims
  The target at which he aims
  Is not to be white
  Because he's proud of his color
  And being called a brother
  His focus will get strong
  Though things will go wrong
  Our struggle must be prolonged
  Because of the shade of our skin
  And the power that lies within

Wisdom increasing
  Ignorance deceasing
  Changing his thinking

From wondering to believing
Outkast said:
"Willing, God willing, all things are the do-able"
His color makes it capable
Because it symbolizes power
Unbreakable
Strength
Invincible

My cousin is dipped in chocolate
　And his afro's growth
　Is the same as his awareness
　About our past
　Happy 'cause his color will always last
　The black cotton field
　That rests on his head
　Is his crown
　And when times get him down
　All he has to do
　Is renew
　His power through the "do"
　And I will teach him
　Things he should know
　As my knowledge grows

He's a star
　That will travel far
　He will shine
　Because God is on his side
　This he is aware
　As his kinky hair
　Grows to the sky
　And his spirit
　Starts to fly
　I watch and smile
　Nearby....

Silly Girl

(For: Sarah Hope Phillips...I love you)

My little cousin of eleven
Thinks she fell from heaven
Smiling up at me
And laughing uncontrollably
But, I love her so much
Just like a gentle touch
Of an angel who always flies
And seldom cries
Always questioning me
And my ability
Yes, she often gets on my nerves
But, my love for her grows
Even if her age sometimes shows
We bicker and scream
But our spirits connect like cookies 'n cream
And, because of her sign
She roars like a feline
But, I wag my head
And open the doors of my heart
'Cause I loved her from the start
8/8/90 I saw her chocolate-colored skin
And ever since then
We've been like twins
She can't deny
How her name came from mine
I tell everyone who asks
About the two princesses
Who always laugh and laugh

She's my little sun
Whose light has always shone
Because her heart is made of roses
And her soul of butterflies
One day we will float to heaven together
So high
Because her heart is made of roses
And her soul of butterflies

To guide your emotions,
Know your heart . . .

Stealer of My Heart

How I refused you
Time after time
I kept to myself
And didn't say a word
But I grinned when your brown eyes
Found mine and held on
For minutes at a time
How I wish I were stronger
October baby
I'm supposed to be balanced
But you changed my astrology
Because you destabilize me
Tried and tried to win my heart
Your charisma and charm
Weakened the stars
That conducted my destiny
Your wicked tongue
Held words that my virgin ears
Had never heard
And when they were spoken
My eyes watered with their beauty
I gave you all of my heart
Expecting yours in return
But you refused me
And ran with my love
The reason is very clear
But I'm still wondering
Why I am waiting here

5:20

If there's anything I hate
It's being stood up
By someone who planned
The rendezvous
And isn't that a silly thing to do?
Wasted time and anxious mind
Ticks like a clock
Striking nine
5:20
And I'm waiting here
Because you're late
I see a person approaching near
Can they change my fate?
I hold my breath
To see if it's you
No, just a lost soul
Wandering about
You've erased my fears
With doubt
Because I relied on you
All the while knowing
You are unreliable
Still I had faith
And wished that you would change
For me today
But it's 5:45
And you're 25 minutes late
I could be home
With some Earl Grey tea

But instead I'm praying
That you're the next one I'll see
Wasted my time
So many ways before
Made me feel special
But still closed the door
Of your heart
When I asked to enter
Since you barged you're way into mine
Without any invite
Now I frown
Now I cry
Never again will I wait
So long
And sing this lonely song
But don't get me wrong
It's not you I hate
I just don't like it that you're late
Time passed
And hours went
Passion and life are now spent
Eight o'clock
And I'm on my way home
Tired of your lies and moods
Never again will I trust in you
So many males would die
To be in your place
Still I sat with an expectant face
I don't understand why I was there
When I knew you never cared
It's only about your habit
Not about me
But eventually
You'll see
How great it could be

To fall in love with a girl like me
Yet you kept me standing
Because your flesh is too demanding
I hope I haunt your mind
And flood your soul
With conviction
Because instead of admittance
You gave me prevention
To get my mind off of this day
And the unproductive time I spent
The feeling compels like cotton with lent
To close my eyes
And think about a Gemini...

Smiles and grins
That come from within
Can't stay inside
Emotions can no longer hide
Because your love
Strengthens me
And now I live happily
Eyes full of life and joy
No reason to be coy
I am now yours to enjoy
But my heart has been stolen
From me
Unwillingly
And I wonder when
I will have it again
I am flying in circles
Not escalating or elevating
But remaining
Yours
Forever....

The Fee of Love Deferred

I thought our love was true
But I didn't know what I was getting into
Still when that boy came my way
All I knew is that I wanted him to stay
And when he said my name
Spit some game
My self-esteem rose
I felt needed so I chose
To try to be his "girl"
See, I was lured by his words
So I swayed my curves
When I passed him by
He didn't even have to try
Because he had already caught my eye
Together, to me, we made
Harmony
Lovers we could always be
Our fast rhythm would never fade
So I thought
But through this I was taught
Not to go by a kiss
Because the objective I will miss
He wanted me for more than I could give
He said if I hadn't done it then I haven't lived
But I knew I was too special
To give up my seed
Because purity is what I need
At the beginning, in my mind

I thought our futures were combined
But I learned so much from this boy:
Not to give my heart so easily
To one who treats me as a toy
Now I know that being by myself
Is what I preferred
This is what happens when love is deferred

Love Me

*P*lease love me
So that I may feel appreciated
Love me for who I am
Not for what I can do for your
Fantasies
I wish you would love me
Enough to fly away with me
So we could race through the clouds
And sleep with the stars
We can laugh with the angels
And feel utmost joy
But are you compelled to my soul?
Let your gentle touch
Turn my frowns into smiles
Cherish my time and make it worthwhile
The moments we could share
Anytime, anywhere
As we fly away
Into the depths of the sky
To race through the clouds
And sleep with the stars
Let's laugh together,
My angel

You can't experience true pleasure without knowing pain.

The Tears of Summer

Forever is a very long time
And I wonder when time will be on my side
Because as it passes by
I ask myself why
I continue loving you
Although you were never true
To your words and promises
People prophesied
Like Nostradomus
That I would end up in tears
After we spent the happy years
I ignored the precautions and advice
That is why I had to pay the price
The fee of love deferred
Although I preferred
For our "relationship" to last
But it's in the past
Like trends
Still trying to be friends?
Yet I moaned with the rains
And cried during sunshine
Now I'm free of pains
And you still aren't mine
I'm aware of the reason
But I will never cry again
During the summer season

Can You Hear Them?

So many times I've held back tears
Lied and lied for so many years
Can you not sense the fears
That always stay in my mind?
Searched and searched but I couldn't find
Why my light would no longer shine
As you look into my fiery eyes,
Can you hear my small cries?

I tried and tried to tell you how I feel
But this nightmare is becoming so real
And I'm apathetic to everything
I'm a caged bird who wants to sing
But my beak is forced to stay closed
So many things I feel remain untold
As you look into my sad eyes,
Can you hear my fretful cries?

I am now at the end of my road
I want to know what to do
I am bearing a heavy load
But I still have to love you
And please don't get me wrong
It's not a difficult task
But you won't let me sing my song
And I'm a little scared to ask:
"But as you look into my empty eyes,
Can you hear my hushed cries?"

Our stars are dying to meet
They have so much to say
But are scared to speak
Instead they shine
And take a peak
Of each other
Every now and then

To Love Once

*I*mpulses
That take over me
Feelings
That encompass my heart
Emotions
That play tricks on my mind
So many times
I gave all of my heart
To someone
Whom I thought deserved it
But there was no reciprocation
I fall too easily
For the ones that show interest
And cause my eyes to glitter
With satisfaction

I've mistaken this "thing"
For love
Over and over again
Because when their eyes fell upon me
I was cast into a spell of hypnosis
There was no more of anything
Just us
And I would lower my eyelids
Because of embarrassment
Then the corners of my lips
Would spread into a grin
And a feeling of warmth
Fled through my veins
But now love is no more

People say,
   "It's better to have loved once than not at all"
   But love brings tears
   Fears and heartache
   Just when I thought I was stronger
   I saw his beautiful face
   And all strength was erased
   Confused thoughts fluttered my mind
   Still I seem to find
   Images of him
   That won't disappear
   And I wish that I wouldn't have to hear
   His name ever again
   So I won't be reminded of my sin:
   Love

To love once makes me not want to love again
   Because love is beautiful pain
   It hurts like a knife through your heart
   Still, it's as beautiful as a white rose
   And together beauty and pain becomes one
   To render love
   The white rose is now tainted with the blood
   That drips from my heart

I question my independence
   Is it strengthening or weakening?
   This can't be true love
   Just a taste of satisfaction
   With connotations
   Of remorse. . . .

Wish I May, Wish I Might...

So many things have changed
   Since the past and yesterday's shame
   I sat trying to loathe your name
   For fear of you doing the same
   But still, I wish you loved me

I told myself to love you no more
   I cried and cried and wonder what for
   I can't bear to have my heart tore
   And my feelings left painfully sore
   But still, I wish you loved me

I wanted to catch your eye
   So everything in my power I tried
   But you didn't ask if you could be mine
   I would've said yes, but how I cried
   Still, I wish you loved me

The salt from the tears kissed my cheek
   And all the mourning made me weak
   I was so drained I could hardly speak
   I could barely stand on my own two feet
   And still, I wish you loved me

I do not wish for much
   But how I longed for you touch
   Now I look in retrospect
   My sorrow did reflect
   The lonely nights and days
   I wished the pain away
   That's what really mattered

All other issues shattered
Yet, I wish you loved me

Because your image seemed to find
  The same space in the corner of my mind
  My emotions weren't stabilized
  But now I have realized
  The more you try to wish someone away
  The more your heart begs them to stay
  My world stopped spinning
  Am I back at the beginning?
  And I wonder where the time went
  Where were all the years spent
  Yes I do regret
  And I wish I'd forget
  But still, I wish you loved me

Mind travels beyond humanity
My thoughts float peacefully
My soul flies lazily
And I smile drowsily
As I fall asleep thinking of you.

Soft Rain

(Dedicated to Lil' Cherice, Candy, and Tiff)

As I listen to the soft rain
Touching and caressing my windowpane
I feel comfort and happiness
But, most of all – tranquility
And there's warmth inside of me
And my thoughts are dancing in my mind
Images of people I seem to find
And I don't want this moment to cease
Because through this silence I gain peace
And I'm wearing a small grin
It's a reflection of how I feel within
Thunder sounds through the air
It touches the leaves and sings in my ear
Sleep is very near
Because my eyelids are becoming heavy
And the beat of my heart is steady
As it coincides with the drops from the sky
Tonight I feel like a lazy butterfly
It's time for me to disappear
Into the night
Oh, how clear
And oh, how right
For me to go to sleep
My teacup is empty
I'm full of cozy chamomile
Purity is what I feel
And now the rain is no more

Will it resume like before?
It is soft rain in my ear
But, now I shall disappear
Disappear
I'm listening to the soft rain in my ear

As I lay in the darkness,
I see little people
Dancing above my head
Are they fairies
Or angels?
Coming to rescue me

Dancing Light

ale moon
In the dark, dark sky
Your light pours through the leaves
Of nearby forest trees
Will you grace my room and kiss my face
As I lay here for hours in the same place?
I'm waiting and anticipating
The treasures you have for me to see
Please enlighten me
With your tranquility
Are my eyes going to dance with your light?
And become secret lovers during the night?
There are no distant sounds
Serenity is what surrounds
And the only thing that echoes in my ear
Is my heartbeat that sounds so clear
Your light is approaching near
And I will wait here
Until we become one in the still atmosphere

Reaching for the Stars

I stood on my tiptoes
    And straightened my elbows
    I extended my fingers
    Hoping to reach high
    Into the dark sky
    It looked so close
    But felt so far
    And that night
    As I reached for the stars,
    I closed my eyes tight
    And held my breath
    Wishing that I might
    Caress the shining light
    That brightened the night
    But all I felt was air
    So I reached harder in despair
    Still, there was nothing there
    But a soft breeze
    That can be seen through the trees
    I began to cry
    Because although I tried,
    I didn't go very high
    I sat on the grass
    And stared into space
    And wondered how they felt
    Some like cotton, some like lace
    But they were in a different place
    Jimmy claimed he reached the moon
    Sally said she could too

Why can't I even touch the stars?
I lied down and wished they weren't so far
And when I awoke
I thought it to be a joke
There was no more night
Just starry light
So I laughed and played
Wishing the stars would stay
And never go away
"Please play with me all day!"
They replied,
"No, we must go"
So I waved goodbye
And wondered why
It had to end so briefly
But I grinned sleepily
As I saw the sun peaking
And it's light leaking
Through the big cotton balls
It poured like waterfalls
I'm gonna tell Jimmy and Sally too
Will they believe it to be true?
I danced with the stars
Which really weren't so far...

Heavy eyelids
Bring serenity
Because of the darkness
In the atmosphere
Everything material
And physical
Disappears
Now the body will enter
Into peace with the stars
It will leave this earth
And travel far
Beyond humanity
Thoughts float with the clouds
Souls fly with the birds
And my eyes are closed

Sarah

*L*ove stories
　　Galore
　　But tears shed
　　No more
　　Because they have
　　Ended
　　And my heart is
　　Suspended
　　In the heavens
　　With the angels of hip hop
　　Professing
　　My happiness
　　Confessing
　　Elevations of my
　　Love and joy
　　Never again will I
　　Depend on a boy

Thanking Him above
　　For the strength of
　　Independence
　　And the wisdom
　　Of self-awareness
　　Because of the kiss
　　From the goddess
　　Of knowledge

Now I'm an example
　　For others to follow
　　Loving

59

Yourself
Realizing
Your worth
Neutralizing
The urge
Valuing
My family
God
And friends
Vowing
To never let this happen again

I'm a princess
Because I'm
His Daughter
No man can put jewels
On my crown
To make me valuable
My worth is intangible
Untouchable
Royalty comes from the core

The essence of my
Origin
Salute to AFRICA
And all the foreign
Nations frowned on by
AMERICA
As my feet trod upon
The ground
I thank my ancestors
In heaven
For making my life easier
And protecting me
With your wings

Permitting
Admitting
Me to fly
I admire
Your sage and guidance
It lifts me higher
Blood and sweat on your brow
On your back
I am allowed
To grow
And one day
When I become
A free soul
And my flesh decays
I'll float on a cloud
And give you a kiss
Living in utmost bliss

Drinking the milk
    from the stars above
    Pouring on me
    Sweet love
    Furthering my
    Passion
    Gift
    Compassion
    My heart deepens
    And ignorance weakens
    Longing
    Hoping
    To be a star in the sky

Praying
    That my friends are true
    As I perceive them to be

Despite my growing
And possible notoriety
I love them so
And if ever we go
Our separate ways
Remember
That a piece of my heart
Is with you always
Thank You

Paternal and maternal influences
Interests
Keep me on track
My appreciation
Gratification
Of you both is escalating
As I thank God
For your love remaining
Thank You

Family
Here and abroad
You render peace
Bringing me
Joy and strength
My prayers are with
You
And my smile
Is in the sky
Shining on you
As the days pass by
Thank You

Acknowledging
  My energy
  Life
  Source of my strength
  His faithfulness
  And never-ending love
  Keeps me rooted
  Divine power
  Knowledge and wisdom
  Jehovah Jireh
  My provider
  My comforter
  My father
  You are amazing
  And beyond words
  Grateful for everyday
  You allow my eyes
  To see the sun rise
  With your love,
  I am hypnotized
  I live to see
  You truly happy
  Not enough words
  To explain
  The impact you have on me
  Thank You

Enemies
  Thank you...
  For not believing in me
  Because with your jealousy
  I was mobilized
  To be free
  I launched into
  The heavenlies

So much more
　　Of me is to be birthed
　　And as my dreams vault
　　Into the sky
　　I remember why
　　I am who I am
　　And where I came from
　　To those less fortunate than I
　　Every night I cry
　　For you
　　To those who need
　　A helping hand
　　I'm on my way
　　Hold on for one more day
　　I continue to pray
　　That God showers
　　His blessings on you

As I live
　　And breathe
　　I must give
　　The reason why I can
　　One day
　　You'll comprehend
　　Understand
　　Why I am who I am
　　Now I just
　　Inhale
　　Exhale
　　The grace of God
　　The essence of His perfection
　　The power of His words
　　And until that day
　　When I see my Creator's face
　　I yearn to grow

Spiritually
Physically
Mentally

When I leave
This place
In which I live
I hope to give
Hope
I want to leave a mark
That signifies
Fulfilled dreams
And when times may seem
Too difficult
Remember me
Look into the sky
And I'll be the brightest star
My cry that sings in
The depths of my soul is—

I want to be a star in the sky
Je voudrais être l'étoile dans le ciel...

Goodnight to all my stars.
Goodnight to all my suns.
Goodnight to all my moons.
Goodnight to all my angels.
I will see you on the brighter side of tomorrow,
for it is time for your eyelids to meet.

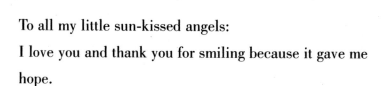

To all my little sun-kissed angels:
I love you and thank you for smiling because it gave me
hope.

Other books by Sarah L. English

The Essence Series:

The Essence of Faith
The Essence of Obedience

Order at www.dontstopdreaming.com

For more information write to:

SLE Publishing
P.O. Box 570795
Dallas, TX 75357
Voice Mail: (888) 485-7040
www.dontstopdreaming.com